Roots and Shoots
and
Wellington Boots

Lois Rock

Illustrations by Helen Herbert

Did you know?

If you take a flower pot, fill it with ordinary garden soil and leave it outdoors where rain will fall on it, plants will grow in it! Even a handful of garden soil hides many seeds just waiting for the right moment to put out roots and shoots.

Did you know?

If you take a pair of wellington boots, wedge them upright between some bricks and leave them outdoors where rain will fall on them, they will soon be full of water.

A LION BOOK

1 Roots and shoots for the unconvinced

Imagine this: you've decided to have a go at growing things. So you get all enthusiastic and put together all the stuff you need. You buy really expensive seeds in a beautiful coloured pack and plant them in really expensive soil. You water the pot with love and care.

Day one, nothing doing. Day two likewise. On day three you decide to organize a search party for the seeds.

'Oh don't do that,' you are told. 'You have to be patient if you want to grow plants.'

Understandably, you're not convinced.

Here's an idea—leave the glamour seeds alone. Try this experiment instead.

Fairly quick roots

You will need

✔ chick peas (you can buy these in a supermarket)

✔ large bowl

✔ sieve

✔ plate

✔ kitchen towel

✔ plastic wrap or a large plastic bag

What to do

1 Take a handful or so of the chick peas and put them in a sieve. Wash under the cold tap for about a minute.

2 Tip the peas in the bowl. Add enough cold water from the tap to cover them. Then add about 3 cm of very hot water. Leave the peas to soak all day or all night.

3 At the sink, tip the soaked peas back into the sieve. Let the water drain away and then rinse under the cold tap for a minute or so. Leave to drain.

4 Line a plate with three layers of kitchen towel. Soak them with water. Tip the beans on top and spread them out. Add three more layers of kitchen towel and sprinkle these with water. Wrap the whole thing lightly in plastic wrap or a large plastic bag.

5 Place the plate in a warm place—in the airing cupboard or near a radiator—for about 8 hours. Unwrap.

6 YES! The peas should have put out wiggly white roots. Positive proof that seeds do grow roots when warm and wet.

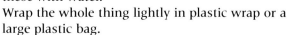

Curried Thing

You will need

- ✔ your handful of sprouted chick peas
- ✔ 30 ml vegetable oil
- ✔ 15 ml curry powder
- ✔ 5 ml salt
- ✔ 100 ml water
- ✔ 1 onion, chopped
- ✔ 2 tomatoes, chopped
- ✔ frying pan with lid
- ✔ wooden spoon

Always remember to check with a grown-up before you try any cooking. You will probably need some help for this recipe.

What to do

1 Get all the ingredients and equipment ready by the stove.

2 Heat the oil in a frying pan. Add the curry powder and stir for about fifteen seconds.

3 Add the onion and tomatoes. Stir for two minutes

4 Add the chick peas. Stir some more.

5 Add the salt and a little water. Stir, stir, stir.

6 Put the lid on the pan. Turn the heat down low and let the mixture simmer for one hour. Check at least every five minutes to make sure there is still a little water left in the pan, and add a bit more if needed.

Curried Thing is a simple form of a traditional Indian dish, and can be served with boiled rice. It is curious tasting but appeals greatly to grown-ups who are desperately trying to get you to stop eating junk food.

Slightly slower shoots

Try saying 'slightly slower shoots' really fast. Keep practising in those long, empty days while the slightly slower shoots are growing.

You will need

- ✔ cress seeds
- ✔ kitchen towel
- ✔ plate
- ✔ water

What to do

1 Line the plate with kitchen towel and moisten with a little water. Sprinkle the cress seeds on top. Put on a windowsill in a warm room.

2 Keep the kitchen towel moist, by sprinkling it with water twice a day.

3 Expect wiggly white roots to appear in about two days. Expect shoots to uncurl from day five onwards. Expect the shoots to be about 5 cm tall with a pair of little green leaves open after nine days.

4 Trim your harvest of cress to add to a green salad or an egg sandwich.

After you have done this page of experiments you may have enough trust in the power of seeds to put out roots and shoots that you can wait a little longer for your garden to grow!

2 In praise of plants

The world of growing plants is a world of everyday miracles.

However clever you get at growing, never forget to stop and look at your plants... enjoy the results... and marvel at how they grow!

Behold a seed: the perfect portable plant unit.

All wrapped up for winter survival strategies.

Carefully programmed to grow whan conditions are warm and wet enough.

Yielding a plant that uses just earth, water and sunshine to produce leaves and flowers and fruit.

Just think how many types of plants there are!

Seed collection

Collect as many seeds as you can. Just look at their shapes and sizes!

Would you believe it?

Which plant grew from which seeds? Do you know? Can you guess? Answers on page 16.

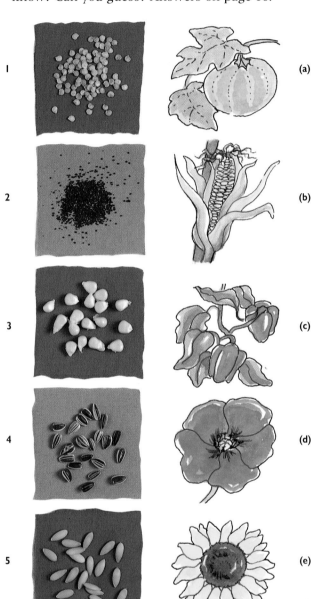

The free garden

Try saving seeds and pips from fruit and vegetables and planting them in a pot of moist soil. Wrap the pot in plastic wrap and keep it in a warm, dark place. Check it every few days to see if the seeds are sprouting. When they do, remove the plastic and let the seedlings grow on in the light.

Great inventions of all time

How did plants begin? Can such a clever design be an accident? How does it happen that the little miracle of seeds producing roots and shoots keeps happening?

From long ago, people have tried to come up with an answer. Here is an ancient creation story that says that a great God designed and made the world. It is from the Bible.

In the beginning, God created heaven and earth... land and sea... day and night. Then God commanded the earth to produce all kinds of plants, and it was done. God was very pleased.

Then God made all kinds of living creatures, fish and birds and animals. Then God made human beings to look after the earth. 'I have provided all kinds of plants for you to eat. There is grain and fruit for you. For the birds and animals there are grasses and leaves,' he said to them.

And God spent time resting and enjoying the beautiful world.

Ever since, people have been marvelling...

'Sowe Carrets in your Gardens, and humbly praise God for them, as for a singular and great blessing.'

PROFITABLE INSTRUCTIONS FOR THE MANURING, SOWING AND PLANTING OF KITCHEN GARDENS (1599)

3 Soil: the stuff of gardening

From tree top to bed rock

Soil is made up of the bedrock of the earth, mixed with the remains of plants great and small. It provides a home to plants and many tiny creatures.

Grab a handful of soil. Spread it out on a sheet of white paper.

Can you find . . .?

★ big bits of stone

★ stone ground down to sand— at least some of this comes from the bedrock

★ bits of rotted plant

★ autumn leaf—from the tree top

★ seeds

★ trailing pieces of root

★ lost toy

Did you know?

In gardens, the topsoil is usually from 15 cm to 70 cm deep.
Wellington boots can be anything from 15 cm about 50 cm deep.

The top layer of soil is called topsoil (surprisingly enough!) It has the most plant material in it, because dead plants fall on the top and rot there.

The next layer down is called subsoil. It has less plant material in it and more ground-up rock.

Eventually you hit bedrock, part of the solid rock of the planet.

Wanted! Soil—dead or alive

Garden shops sell large bags of soil. Usually, this has been sterilized: treated so that there is nothing left living or growing in it.

If you plunk a few handfuls of garden soil in a pot and keep it warm and moist, all kinds of plants will begin to grow.

Try this experiment:

You will need

✔ two pots

✔ garden soil

✔ sterilized soil

✔ two large transparent plastic bags

✔ twine or twist ties

✔ wood or plastic labels

✔ garden pen

What to do

1 Put garden soil in one pot and sterilized soil in the other. Water the soil. Put a label in each pot to say which is which.

2 Put the pots in plastic bags and tie these almost closed.

3 Leave both the pots out of doors. Open the bags and water the pots occasionally to make sure the soil never dries out.

4 Watch the results.

Once you have seen for yourself the difference in what grows, try leaving the pot of sterilized soil in the open. Over a few months it may well grow lots of plants. Seeds will be blown into it by the wind or dropped on to it by birds.

Weeds

Weeds are the hardy pioneers of the plant world. Some plants are softies: they need the right kind of soil, poor dears, and just the right kind of temperature, and just the right amount of water. Weeds don't care. Just a glimpse of the soil, and they make themselves at home. In what seems like no time, they've surrounded themselves with relatives.

The amazing root trick

Some plants can grow new versions of themselves from small bits of root. That little trick makes it hard to get rid of certain types of weed. Somehow, there's always a tiny bit left in the soil.

You will need

✔ a pot of sterilized soil

✔ a piece of root from the type of weed that comes up year after year. Try dandelion or bindweed.

What to do

1 Bury the root deep in the sterilized soil.

2 Water the pot. Put it in a plastic bag and tie up the top. Keep it warm and moist.

3 Here it comes!

Now you've done this page, you may be able to say why gardeners have to keep weeding over and over again (or see page 16).

4 Water and light

Plants need water. Plants need light.
Here are two experiments to show how desperate they are
if they don't have them.

Cress in distress

Each of these pots was filled with soil and cress
seeds were sprinkled on top.
   But they didn't get the same treatment.

Look at the results:

Why not try this
experiment yourself?

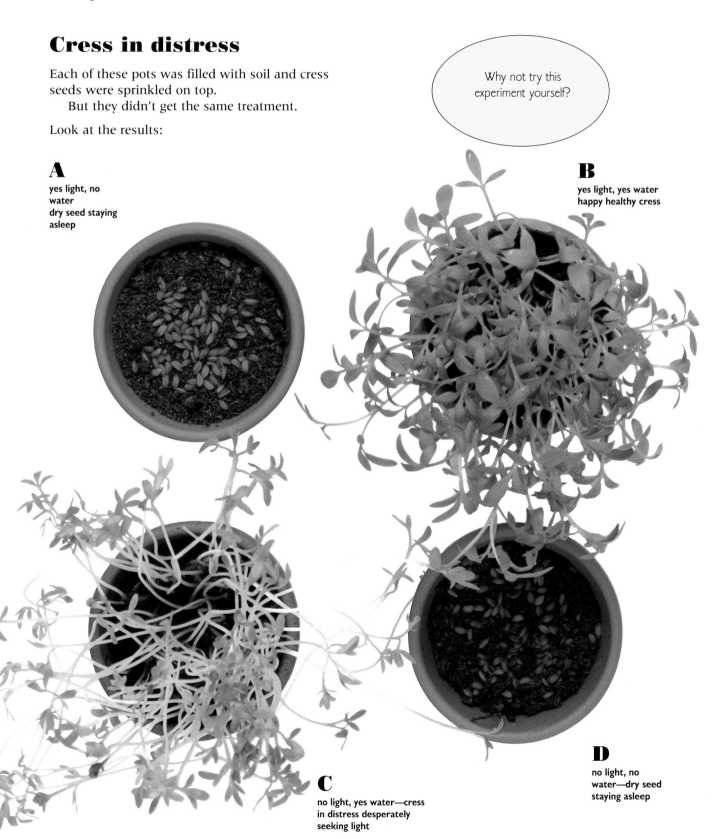

A
yes light, no
water
dry seed staying
asleep

B
yes light, yes water
happy healthy cress

C
no light, yes water—cress
in distress desperately
seeking light

D
no light, no
water—dry seed
staying asleep

Houdini the Bean

And now, to demonstrate, the incredible, astonishing feats of daring by that brilliant contortionist and escapologist— Houdini the Bean!

For Houdini, we have prepared a dark green bottle, with just 3 cm of moist soil in the bottom. We add a little water.

Houdini is hurling himself into the soil.

We hide the bottle in a box that has a tiny hole cut in it.

We leave Houdini on a windowsill, with the hole facing the window.

Every day we check on Houdini. We add a little water.

Weeks later, to huge public acclaim...

HOUDINI THE BEAN FINDS THE LIGHT!

A straggly, yellow light-starved plant may never **fully** recover! But leave it in the light—and watch how quickly the leaves turn green.

Pots and plots

Where will you have a garden?
A pot is all you need! But if you have a garden, perhaps you can have a small plot of your own.

Self-contained

Create a garden from an array of pots on a sunny windowsill, balcony or patio.

You can buy:

★ clay pots

★ plastic pots

★ saucers to catch drips from the bottom hole

★ plant labels

★ waterproof gardening pen

Or you can use leftover containers:

★ plastic pots (snip the base to allow water to drain away)

★ ancient wellington boots (ask a grown up to make a hole or two in the base, to allow water to drain away)

★ slightly cracked plastic sandpit

★ ancient plates and saucers to catch water that drips from the hole

★ labels cut from white plastic containers

★ wooden sticks

If your household seems to get a lot of white plastic containers, you could cut lots of labels from them as a gift for enthusiastic gardeners.

Paper planters

These papier mâché bowls will cover up the nastiest of plastic pots, and will last well indoors. Thy're not really waterpoof so make sure you put the pots with drainage holes in another pot to catch the drips—and use the planter as a decoration only.

You will need

✔ scrap paper such as newspaper or photocopy paper

✔ a large plastic bowl

✔ wallpaper paste

✔ balloons

✔ wire rack

What to do

1 Tear the paper into squares about 3 cm x 3 cm.

2 Blow up the ballons and tie.

3 Put a little warm water in the plastic bowl. Shake in wallpaper paste and stir till the liquid is thick like cream.

4 Dip the paper in the paste and stick all over the balloon to make a bowl shape. Make sure the pieces overlap. Apply at least two layers all over.

5 Put on the rack and leave to dry for a day or so. Then add two more layers of paste-soaked paper and leave to dry.

6 Prick the balloon to burst it. Trim the balloon edge if needed and paste squares to bind the edge. Apply a layer inside as well.

7 While the shape is damp, squidge the base flat so that the planter stands firm. Leave it to dry on the rack.

8 Paint inside and out with acrylic paints. Make the outside as decorative as you like.

Garden plot

A garden plot needs:

★digging with a spade, so the soil is clear of weeds and easy to rake

★raking till the soil is fine and crumbly

★constant weeding—using a trowel to winkle out roots

★sturdy sticks for use as row markers and labels

The indoor jungle

Decorate your home with fabulous pot plants.

Many places will sell you houseplants, and that's one way to collect them. But a lot of plants produce 'babies', and friends are usually very happy to give their babies to a good home.

When your plant is big enough, you can create new plants to give to your friends.

SPIDER PLANTS
like a warm, damp place. When they are big enough, they put out stems with baby plants on. Encourage each baby to put down roots in a pot of moist soil. After about 3 weeks it will be ready to be snipped from the parent plant.

PELARGONIUMS
have thick fleshy stems. This helps them survive drought, when no one bothers to water them. When a pelargonium gets large enough, try nipping off bits of stem about 10 cm long. Pull off a couple of leaves at the base and put the stems into a pot of moist soil, far enough down to cover the leaf scar. Many of these stems will put out roots, and eventually new shoots.

RUNNER BEANS
will grow from seeds—which you can buy, or collect from a ripe pod. You will need a large pot for a runner bean, and you should sow the seed in the spring. In the dim light of indoors (compared with outdoors) they'll grow exotically long and leggy for a season. Give them a pole to twine around.

Caring for houseplants

Find out what conditions they like best: damp or dry, sunny or shady.

For most plants, it's best to let the soil get almost dry before you water it.

Pull off any brown or yellow leaves.

Jungle birds

These will brighten up your jungle!

You will need

✔ coloured paper or thin card

✔ sticky tape

✔ scissors

✔ felt markers

✔ stickers

✔ flower sticks or thin bamboo canes

What to do

1 Cut bird shapes as shown.

2 Tape the two sides together.

3 Decorate your bird.

4 Add paper tail feathers, as exotic as you like.

5 Tape your bird to a stick. Push the stick into a plant pot, so the bird sits among the foliage.

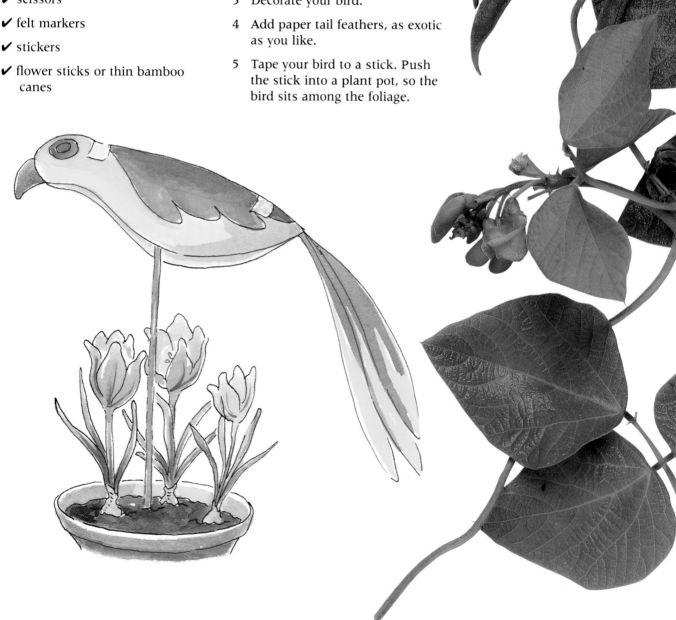

7 Summer flowers

Growing a summer flower garden is something you have to start in spring, when the days are getting longer and warmer.

Plants that feel the cold

Some flowers, such as petunias and nicotiana, come from warmer countries and feel the cold of spring. But you can start growing them indoors in early spring. By early summer you will have little plants ready to grow.

You will need

✔ a pot of soil

✔ plastic wrap

✔ flower seeds

and for later...

✔ larger containers of soil

✔ a pencil-sized stick

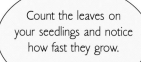
Count the leaves on your seedlings and notice how fast they grow.

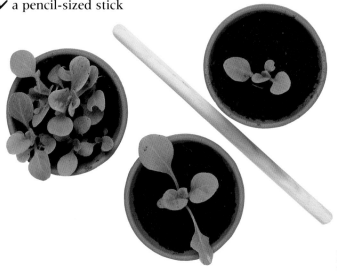

What to do

1 Sprinkle the seeds in a pot of soil. Cover with plastic wrap and put the pots in a warm place to grow.

2 When the seedlings appear, remove the wrap and let the plants grow on in the light.

3 When they have two to four true leaves (not the first, baby leaves) they need more room.
Fill a larger container with soil, and use the pencil-sized stick to mark holes in the soil, each about 3 cm apart.

4 Use the stick to loose the soil in the pot of seedlings. Hold each seedling gently by a baby leaf to pull it away and replant it in a hole in the larger container. Firm the soil around it.

5 When the container is full, water it gently. Let the plants grow on.

6 On warm days, let the container stand outdoors for a few hours.

7 When all risk of frost is passed, leave the container out longer—and eventually overnight as well.

8 When the plants are too big for the container, plant them out into your garden pots or plots.

Water pots every day in summer. Water the garden plot, too, if there is little or no rain.

Hardy plants

Some flowers are hardy enough to be planted direct into the soil in mid spring. Sprinkle soil over the seeds and be sure to mark where you put them! Try:

★ nasturtiums

★ cornflowers

★ godetia

Fill a pot with soil and lightly sprinkle seeds over the surface. Then sprinkle a few handfuls of soil on top to cover the seeds. Keep moist.

In the garden plot, it can be a good idea to sow seeds in rows.

Or you can mark tiny 'fields' using string and twigs for a fence. Scatter the seeds in the field.

Weed plots little and often. If your plants seem too crowded, nip off some to leave more room for the rest to grow.

8 Things to do with flowers

Sniff them

Watch butterflies dancing over them

Pick them and put them in vases

Make tiny posies to give as a gift

1 Tie flowers in a bunch.

2 Cut a paper collar. Wrap it around posy and tape edges.

3 If you wish, wrap stems with florist's tape.

Press them

Press them between sheets of paper, weighted down with books. Leave them several weeks to dry. (You can add to your pile of pressings all through the summer, and return to make use of them in the autumn.)

Pressed flower cards

You will need

- ✔ card
- ✔ glue stick
- ✔ sticky back transparent plastic
- ✔ pressed flowers

What to do

1 Arrange your flowers on the card. When you have got the arrangement right, glue each flower gently in place. Dab the glue on the paper and press the flower on to it.

2 Cover with sticky back plastic.

3 Make cards, bookmarks, pictures and picture frames to give as gifts.

9 Salad bowls

The growing bowl

Grow your salad in one bowl. Then harvest it and toss it in another, ready for eating!

You will need

✔ a large pot of soil

✔ lettuce seeds

✔ radish seeds

✔ carrot seeds (round carrots or short, stumpy carrots are best for pot growing)

✔ water

✔ a large plastic bag, big enough to put the pot in.

✔ an old pencil or stick, for poking holes in the soil

What to do

1 Make holes in the soil with your stick and sow two to three seeds in each thus:

  lettuce in the centre

  carrots at twelve o'clock, three, six and nine!

  radishes between carrots

2 Water the soil gently.

3 Carefully put the pot in a plastic bag, and tie the top shut. Leave in a warm place for a few days.

4 Once the seeds begin to grow, move the pot to a light and sunny place. Keep the soil moist by watering it.

5 When the plants have four 'true' leaves, select the strongest one from each growing hole. Nip off the other one, to give your best plant more room.

6 Plants will be ready to harvest in about 8 weeks.

The tossing bowl

You will need

✔ 1 lettuce

✔ 4 small carrrots

✔ 4 plump radishes

✔ 1 tablespoon oil

✔ 2 tablespoons vinegar

✔ salt

✔ a glass jar with a lid

✔ knife

✔ grater

What to do

1   Wash the lettuce under cold running water and shake dry. Put the leaves in a salad bowl.

2   Scrub the carrots. Chop off the top and bottom end and grate them. Add to the salad bowl.

3   Prepare grated radish in the same way and add to the bowl.

4   Put the oil, vinegar and salt into the jar. Shake hard for a few seconds. Pour the dressing over the salad.

The plot thickens

You can, of course, plant salad vegetables in a small plot. One easy arrangement is to plant in rows.

What to do

1   Mark the end of each row with a stick.

2   Use a trowel to make a groove running in a straight line between the sticks.

3   Sprinkle seeds along the row.

4   Gently cover over the seeds and water.

5   It is easer to spot seedlings when you see lots of the same sort growing along the line! Be sure to weed out anything else.

Another good use for a crop of salad!

Alpine strawberries, mini bush tomatoes and peppers are all wonderfully easy fruits to grow in a pot or plot.

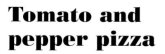

Give them a tender start, following the instructions for tender plants on page 7. Grow them in pots or plots. Keep them well watered.

The best part is harvesting your crop!

Tomato and pepper pizza

Quick pizza base

You will need

- ✔ 250 g flour
- ✔ 5 ml salt
- ✔ 50 g margarine
- ✔ milk
- ✔ extra flour
- ✔ bowl
- ✔ spoon
- ✔ rolling pin
- ✔ baking tray lined with baking parchment

What to do

1 Put the flour, salt and margarine into a bowl. Break the margarine into tiny bits and work them into the flour with your fingertips, until the mixture looks a bit like breadcrumbs.

2 Add the milk a tablespoon at a time. Stir each time, until the mixture begins to cling together. Use your hands to shape the mixture into a lump of dough.

3 Sprinkle a little extra flour on a clean work-surface. Roll the lump of dough into a circle. Fold the dough gently over the rolling pin and lift it onto the baking tray

Pizza filling

You will need

- ✔ jar of pizza sauce or tin of chopped tomatoes
- ✔ tomatoes
- ✔ peppers
- ✔ 150 g mozzarella cheese
- ✔ knife
- ✔ chopping board
- ✔ grater

What to do

1 Preheat the oven to 200°C/Gas Mark 6.

2 Spread the pizza sauce over the pizza base. Or drain the chopped tomatoes, and spread them over the base.

3 Slice your tomatoes and peppers thinly. Arrange them over the sauce.

4 Grate the cheese. Spinkle over the top of the pizza.

5 Place the pizza in the oven and bake for 8 minutes. Then turn the heat to 150°C/Gas Mark 2 and bake for 6 minutes more.

6 Use oven mitts to lift your pizza out of the oven.

Strawberry dessert

You will need

- ✔ 1 cup of cream
- ✔ 1 cup of yoghurt
- ✔ 10 ml caster sugar
- ✔ 1/2 - 1 cup alpine strawberries, washed
- ✔ bowl
- ✔ whisk
- ✔ spoon

What to do

1 Put the cream and sugar in a bowl. Whisk until the cream is stiff.

2 Stir in the yoghurt.

3 Lightly crush the strawberries and stir them in to the cream mixture.

Waste not, want not

Make the most of kitchen and garden waste and you can reap a rich harvest in the garden plot!

A compost heap

You'll need lots of waste to make a compost heap—and it takes a long time to rot down. But if you have a large enough garden to make compost, you'll have an easy way of making a natural fertilizer to give you better crops.

Choose a place for the compost heap. A heap needs to be about a metre square and a metre and a half high to really get going!

Sides to hold the rubbish in are useful. Here is a design you could help a grown-up to build.

On the heap put:

★ grass clippings

★ the tops of weeds (Don't include weeds that have seed heads, or the seeds may grow. Throw away roots, which can grow a new weed.)

★ fruit and vegetable peelings

★ old tea leaves and coffee grounds

★ droppings from vegetarian pets (rabbits, guinea pigs, gerbils...)

In come:

★ worms

★ creepy crawlies

★ bacteria

And the whole heap begins to crumble away to make:

★ rich dark compost

Harvest galore

For a fabulous harvest you can't do better than grow curcubits. Cucumbers, courgettes, marrows, pumpkins and gourds are all curcubits. Courgettes and pumpkins are easy ones to start with.

You will need

✔ small pots of soil

✔ small plastic bags

✔ courgette or pumpkin seeds

✔ water

✔ a plastic bottle, with the bottom cut off

What to do

1   Put one seed in each pot of soil.

2   Water gently.

3   Put each pot in a plastic bag and leave in a warm place.

4   When the seeds start to grow, take the pots out of the bags and put them in a sunny place to grow on.

Outside, prepare a cosy home for the plants. For each...

1   Dig a hole large enough to stand in with wellington boots on.

2   Stand the bottle in the hole with the pouring end facing down.

3   Surround with compost or manure.

4   Put the soil back on top—but make sure the rim of the bottle is still showing, and don't let any soil fall inside.

5   When the days are sunny and warm, and the winter frosts are over, plant your shoots at the top of each mound.

6   Water all over gently.

7   Wait one week. Then, when the plant is growing strongly in its new home, water every day by filling the plastic bottle to the top with water and letting it drain away.

Fertilizing

The plants below sometimes need help to make fruits.

Female flowers have a tiny 'fruit' behind the flower head. Keep these safe.

'Male' flowers do not have a baby fuit. Pick these, pull back the petals, and dust the pollen from the male flower inside the female.

Soon the fruits will start to swell.

For courgettes: pick the fruits as soon as they are 4-12 cm long. Many more will form.

For pumpkins: select the two best fruits on the plant. Lift these gently onto a bed of straw. Cut off any other fruits.

Keep watering week after week while the pumkin grows huge.

Two recipes for a harvest supper, using your curcubit glut. Always remember to check with an adult before you start any cooking.

Courgette cake

When a courgette plant starts producing courgettes, it doesn't know how to stop. Use some of the produce in this cake. Leave people to guess what the green flecks really are...

You will need

- ✔ 2 courgettes (about 200 g together)
- ✔ 3 eggs
- ✔ 250 ml vegetable oil
- ✔ 5 ml vanilla essence
- ✔ 400 g plain flour
- ✔ 10 ml baking powder
- ✔ 5 ml salt
- ✔ 10 ml cinnamon
- ✔ 2 ml nutmeg
- ✔ 100 g sultanas

What to do

1. Preheat the oven to 170°C/Gas Mark 5.
2. Wash the courgettes. Grate them.
3. Crack the eggs into a bowl and beat them.
4. Sift the flour, baking powder, cinnamon and nutmeg over the mix. Stir them in lightly.
5. Stir in the sultanas.
6. Line two loaf tins with greaseproof paper. Divide the mixture between the two.

7. Bake for 45 minutes. Use oven mitts to lift the loaves out of the oven.
8. Check that they are done by putting a clean, sharp knife into the centre of the cakes. If the knife blade is clean when you pull it out, the cake is done. If not, put the cakes back in the oven for a few more minutes.
9. Remember to turn the oven off.
10. The loaf is best served cut into thick slices and spread with butter.

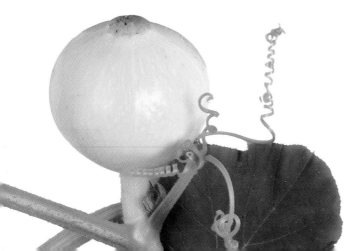

Pumpkin soup

Here's how to use the flesh of your pumpkin and leave the 'shell' whole:

✔ Slice off the top.

✔ Use a large, strong, metal tablespoon to scoop out the seeds.

✔ Now dig harder with the spoon to carve out long strips of flesh.

You will need

25 g butter

1 onion

2 carrots

1 kg pumpkin flesh

500 ml water

salt and pepper

5 ml ground cardamom

150 ml milk or cream

What to do

1 Peel and chop the onion and the carrots.

2 Melt the butter in a large saucepan on top of the stove. Add the chopped carrots and onion. Keep the heat low, and stir the vegetables in the butter for about five minutes.

3 Add the pumpkin and cardamom. Stir for another five minutes.

4 Add the water and some salt and pepper (try a teaspoonful of salt and a pinch of pepper to begin with).

5 Bring the water to the boil, then turn the heat down and let the vegetables simmer for about 24 minutes.

6 Turn off the heat. Using oven mitts, lift the pan on to a heatproof surface. Allow to cool for about 15 minutes.

7 Carefully ladle the mixture in small batches into a food processor or blender. Whizz until smooth and creamy. When each batch is done, tip it into a clean saucepan.

8 Put the mixture back on the stove and turn on a low heat. Stir the soup gently until it is just beginning to boil.

9 Turn off the heat. Lift the saucepan on to a heatproof surface. Stir in 150 ml of milk or cream.

13 The wildlife bush

A wildlife garden is a wonderful thing: full of creepy-crawlies, butterflies and birds.

Grow your own wildlife bush

For a start in wildlife gardening, try this wonderful wildlife bush.

You will need

✔ one buddleia bush

You can get this by

1   Growing one from seeds.

2   Taking a cutting. (Take several pieces of young stem from a bush pull off the lowest two leaves and stick the stripped end in a pot of soil. After a few months, some will have put out roots. They will begin to grow.)

3   Buy a buddleia. Put it in a large pot or in a small plot of earth. Put a pile of stones nearby.

IN THE SPRING:
When leaves start to sprout, cut the buddleia quite short—but leave a few strong spouting bits.

IN THE LATE SUMMER: The flower spikes come out. Masses of butterflies are attracted by the smell, and come to sip nectar from the flowers.

IN THE SUMMER:
Watch the stems grow tall. Lift up the stones from time to time, to see what creepy-crawlies are making their home amongst them.

IN THE AUTUMN:
The leaves will fall. Leave a few for creepy-crawlies to nest among.

IN THE WINTER:
Hang food for the birds among the branches.
In the spring, cut down... and begin the process all over again!

14 Spring will come again...

Autumn in the garden. . . frost in the air.

Before you scrub the mud off your welly boots and snuggle up indoors for the winter, its time to get ready for next spring.

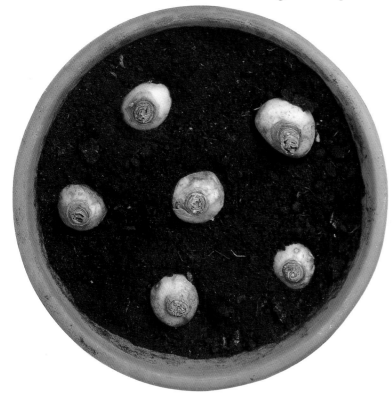

Bulbs

Plant spring bulbs in a pot of earth. Choose early-flowering crocuses, bright daffodils, cheerful tulips.

Easter Extravaganza

Easter is a time when Christians celebrate new life. They celebrate an amazing event in the life of a man named Jesus who lived two thousand years ago. Jesus had spent three years telling people about God—and showing God's love and healing. His enemies had him killed, and he was buried in a tomb. Three days later, the tomb was open—and Jesus' friends saw him alive.

Christians believe that God gives new life to anyone who follows Jesus, that all the bad and sad things that make life feel like winter for ever are beaten.

This is their good news. And it's hardly surprising they use flowers to decorate the church buildings where they celebrate—flowers that have sprung up from the depths of the earth after the dead of winter.

For Easter blooms...

1 Plant bulbs in a pot of earth. Cover with soil. Put on a layer as thick as the bulb is tall.

2 Water your pot of bulbs well and leave outdoors, in the cold and rain.

3 Daffodils are your best bet for blooms when Easter is in March. If Easter is in April, put in April-flowering narcissi and tulips!

For winter cheer

If you want bulbs extra early, put your pot of bulbs in a cool, dark place such as a shed, inside a lightly-knotted plastic bag.

After six weeks, begin checking every week for shoots.

When the shoots are about 10 cm tall, bring the plants into the light. Leave them outdooors or in an unheated room till the flower bud is visible.

Then bring them into a warm place and watch them unfold.

They won't last long, but they bring cheer on a dark day.

Happy Christmas

You'll want to take a break from heavy gardening at Christmas, so you can join in all the celebrations. But you can still have fun with roots and shoots and wellington boots.

Mini trees

Evergreens at Christmas bring good cheer. Christians remember the birth of the baby Jesus, come to bring God's love and God's peace to this world. Love that keeps on growing even when people are cruel and unkind, just as evergreens stay green in the harsh winter weather.

Grow your own little Christmas trees, You can buy seeds for a variety of evergreen trees—or you can try picking the winged seeds out of a pine cone and growing those.

Or you can buy a tiny tree.

Don't chop it down! Put it in a straight sided pot and decorate that for Christmas.

1   Cut strips of craft foil big enough to wrap around the pot. Arrange in bands, taping the ends together.

2   If you wish, snip the top edge into points.

3   Fold the points over elegantly.

Leaf cards

Collect leaves before they fly away in late autumn and use them to make leaf prints. Then turn them into elegant Christmas cards.

You will need

- ✔ flat leaves
- ✔ paint
- ✔ a brush
- ✔ white paper
- ✔ two wads of old newspaper
- ✔ coloured card

What to do

1 Cut the paper into neat squares, large enough to take a leaf print. Put them ready by the side of one of the wads of newspaper.

2 On the other wad, paint the ridged side of the leaf.

3 Now lift the leaf on to the clean wad, paint side still upwards. Lay one clean sheet of white paper on top, and rub gently all over with your finger. Take care not to move the paper while you do this.

4 Lift up the paper and peel the leaf away.

5 Throw away the top sheets of newspaper, so the next clean sheet below is ready for your next print. You can use the same leaf for printing several times. but it's fun to use lots of different leaf shapes. You can vary the colours of your paint as you like.

6 Turn your best prints into greetings cards by cutting a print out and gluing it on to a piece of folded card. Send cards to people you love, and also to people who need to know they have a friend at this gloomy time of year.

Festive boots

Decorate a pair of welly boots, and put them at the foot of the bed on Christmas night. Perhaps they will be filled with gifts the following morning!

What to do

1 Clean up an an old pair of boots, leave them to dry and then paint bright designs on them using acrylic paint.

2 Or you can clean up your everyday boots and jazz them up with stickers for the big event! You can peel the stickers off afterwards, or let them wear off in the mud and rain!

The complete gardener has:

★ old clothes

★ gloves to protect the hands from cuts and stings

★ boots to give good grip on mud

★ goggles at the ready for weeding among spiky plants

and:

★ keeps tools neatly arranged so people don't fall over them, into them, on them or under them

The complete indoor gardener has:

★ apron

★ dibber

★ old tray to catch dirt

Cooking

★ Always ask a grown up before you do any cooking.

★ Wear flat shoes, and an apron to cover your clothes.

★ Use oven mitts when handling anything hot.

Answers

Page 2

1(c): pepper
2(d): poppy
3(b): sweetcorn

4(e): sunflower
5(a): melon

Page 3

Weeds come from:
★ seeds in the soil
★ seeds brought in by birds, animals and the wind
★ roots and bits of root in the soil

Copyright © 1996 Lois Rock
This edition copyright © 1996 Lion Publishing
Illustrations copyright © 1996 Helen Herbert

Photographs by John Williams Studios.
Butterfly (spread 13): Lion Publishing/David Alexander
Copyright © Lion Publishing.

The author asserts the moral right
to be identified as the author of this work

Published by
Lion Publishing plc
Sandy Lane West, Oxford, England
ISBN 0 7459 3131
Albatross Books Pty Ltd
PO Box 320, Sutherland, NSW 2232, Australia
ISBN 0 7324 1272 2

First edition 1996

10 9 8 7 6 5 4 3 2 1 0

Printed in Hong Kong

Index